the **best** of
FILLING &
Healthy

WeightWatchers®
the best of FILLING & *Healthy*

Over **40** of your **FAVOURITE** recipes including **ALL** of our *approaches*

**SIMON &
SCHUSTER**

London · New York · Sydney · Toronto · New Delhi

A CBS COMPANY

the recipes

 ProPoints values: You'll find a **ProPoints** value beside every recipe in this book. This tells you how many **ProPoints** values per serving each recipe contains.

Filling & Healthy Foods: We highlight all of our Filling & Healthy foods in green. These foods are at the heart of our plan so eat them whenever you can – they will help to fill you up faster and keep you fuller for longer.

 This means you can freeze this dish. There may be specific freezing instructions so just check the recipe to be sure.

 If you see this symbol beside a recipe, it means that healthy oils (olive, safflower, sunflower, flaxseed or rapeseed) have been used – remember, if you're following the Filling & Healthy day approach and you have already used your 2 daily teaspoons, you'll need to count this out of your weekly allowance.

the small print

EGGS We use medium eggs, unless otherwise stated. Pregnant women, the elderly and children should avoid recipes with eggs which are not fully cooked or raw.

FRUIT AND VEGETABLES Our recipes use medium-sized fruit and veg unless otherwise stated.

LOW FAT SOFT CHEESE Where a recipe uses low fat soft cheese, we mean a soft cheese with a fat content of less than 5%.

LOW FAT SPREAD When a recipe uses a low fat spread, we mean a spread with a fat content of no less than 38%.

MICROWAVES If we have used a microwave in any of our recipes, the timings will be for an 850 watt microwave oven.

PREP AND COOKING TIMES These are approximate and meant to be guidelines. Prep time includes all the steps up to and following the main cooking time(s). Cooking times may vary according to your oven. Before serving chicken, always check that there is no pink meat and that the juices run clear by piercing with a sharp knife or skewer.

The use of the terms 'gluten free' or the 'gluten free icon' is illustrative only. Weight Watchers is not responsible for the presence of gluten in dishes that have not been prepared in accordance with instructions; nor is it responsible for gluten contamination due to any external cause. Recipes labelled as gluten free, or displaying the gluten free icon, only include ingredients that naturally do not contain gluten. Whenever using canned, bottled or other types of packaged processed ingredients, such as sauces and stocks, it is essential to check that those ingredients do not contain gluten.

First published in Great Britain by Simon & Schuster UK Ltd, 2015
A CBS Company

Copyright © 2015, Weight Watchers International, Inc.

Simon & Schuster UK Ltd
222 Gray's Inn Road
London WC1X 8HB
www.simonandschuster.co.uk
Simon & Schuster Australia, Sydney
Simon & Schuster India, New Delhi

This book is copyright under the Berne Convention.
No reproduction without permission.
All rights reserved.

10 9 8 7 6 5 4 3 2 1

Weight Watchers, **ProPoints** and the **ProPoints** icon are the registered trademarks of Weight Watchers International Inc. and used under license by Weight Watchers (UK) Ltd. All rights reserved.

Weight Watchers Publications Team:
Imogen Prescott, Stephanie Teed

Recipes by: Sue Ashworth, Kate Blinman, Tamsin Burnett-Hall, Rachel Carter, Anna Crane, Jassy Davis, Nicola Graimes, Lizzie Harris, Catherine Hill, Jennie Milsom, Kim Morphew, Laura Rogers, Penny Stephens

Photography by: Steve Baxter, Terry Benson, Tony Briscoe, Mike English, Will Heap, Lara Holmes, Dan Jones, Jonathan Kennedy, Gareth Morgans, David Munns, Stuart Ovenden, Lis Parsons

For Simon & Schuster
Senior Commissioning Editor: Nicky Hill
Art Director: Corinna Farrow
Production Manager: Katherine Thornton
Design: Miranda Harvey

Colour Reproduction by Aylesbury Studios Ltd, UK
Printed and bound in Italy

A CIP catalogue record for this book is available from the British Library

ISBN: 978-1-47114-902-3

Pictured on front cover, clockwise from top left: Steak with colcannon, page 20; Chunky chilli bean soup, page 68; Quorn tikka salad, page 72; Raspberry jelly creams, page 88

Weight Watchers & the FILLING & Healthy approach ♥

Making the most of this cookbook

If you're following a Filling & Healthy approach, then you're in luck
– every recipe in this book has been selected specially for you! We
have trawled through our cookbook and *Weight Watchers Magazine*
archives to bring you the best, and most favoured, Filling & Healthy
recipes. We've got proper traditional dishes, quick and easy ones, and
a few exotic ones too. And all of them are made up entirely of Filling &
Healthy foods, plus the odd flavour booster, so you can eat your way
through every delightful dish knowing that you won't need to count
anything at all. Plus, if you're following a gluten free approach, fancy
a bit of a Mediterranean take on things, or want to reduce your carbs
for a while, then we have marked these up for you as well so you can
eat exactly how you like. Your way.

ProPoints values

If you are counting, then keep an eye out for the **ProPoints** bucket.
Inside will be a number which tells you the **ProPoints** values of each
serving and therefore how many you'll need to use from your daily
allowance. This makes it really easy to follow the plan while cooking
from scratch, as there is no guesswork involved.

Eating your way

So whether you're counting, or not; are properly into your pasta; or
just fancy a bit of Med sunshine flavour in your life, then this book will
bring you lots of joy in the kitchen and lots of love to the table.

Find out more at www.weightwatchers.co.uk

Filling & Healthy day approach

A great way to get focused on your weight loss. And an alternative way to follow the plan if you don't want to weigh, measure and count everything. The Filling & Healthy day approach introduces you to an alternative to counting the *ProPoints* values of everything you eat and drink. You simply focus your eating on our list of hundreds of Filling & Healthy foods. These foods help to fill you up faster, stay fuller for longer and avoid the types of foods that can lead to overeating. The recipes in this book are perfect for when you're following this approach. Let the little green heart be your guide.

Gluten Free approach

This approach will steer you to food choices that are naturally gluten free. The *ProPoints* plan is flexible enough to accommodate all your gluten free choices. To make it easy we've flagged the recipes in this book that are suitable for the gluten free approach; but with some of the ingredients used please do make sure you check the product labels (we've pointed out where) – sometimes a cheeky little stock cube, soy sauce or even ketchup can contain gluten.

Higher Carb approach

Passionate about pasta? Can't live without daily bread? Here's how to have your cake and eat it. If you love your carbs, we'll help you make smarter choices for healthy weight loss. There's no need to deny yourself, whether you're on a Filling & Healthy day or counting your daily allowance. Fill your plate with wholewheat pasta and know you're on safe ground with baked spuds. Opt for wholewheat and wholegrain every time: it's easy to embrace your complex carbs. We've made it easy for you to find the higher carb recipes in this book by using the HC icon. Check out the delicious Spiced Cottage Pie with Parsnip Mash on page 22 for a carb-tastic dinner.

Mediterranean approach

Serve up sunshine on a plate. For fresh, delicious food, simply served and bursting with flavour, take a Mediterranean approach to your meals and snacks. This is a great approach if you love fish. Focus on our delicious meal ideas, serving up at least two fish dishes in your week with salads or a large bowl of veg. Opt for desserts and snacks of fresh fruit and natural yogurt and use healthier olive oil instead of butter. Flick to page 32 for a Med-inspired lunch.

Lower Carb approach

Try our lower carb, higher protein recipes for a lighter way to healthy weight loss. We're talking lower carbs here, not no carbs, as it's important to include some carbs in your eating every day. This approach is about lighter carbs and more of a focus on satisfying proteins. Go for lean cuts of meat such as fillet steak and skinless chicken breasts, or opt for Quorn, and combine with large servings of vegetables or salad. We've included some pretty tasty lower carb recipes in this book – you only need to look out for the LC icon to see what we mean.

Vegetarian approach

Whether you're a lifelong vegetarian or a part-timer – it can taste good to go meat-free. We've got loads of vegetarian recipes in this book; and if it's not got a little V icon bedside the recipe, check out the Cook's tips and Variations at the bottom of the recipe – it may be that we've given you an idea for swapping out the meat, meaning you can try out even more of the recipes in the book.
Note: Where relevant, free-range eggs, vegetarian cheese, vegetarian virtually fat-free fromage frais, vegetarian low fat crème fraîche and vegetarian low fat yogurts are used. Virtually fat-free fromage frais, low fat crème fraîche and low fat yogurts may contain traces of gelatine, so they are not always suitable for a vegetarian diet – just check the labels.

Quick guide to the best of FILLING & Healthy

Baked banana with passion fruit **90**

Warm summer berries with raspberry sauce **92**

Thai vegetable broth **70**

Raspberry jelly creams **88**

Chilli lime salmon & prawn skewers **58**

Beanie burgers with salsa **82**

Singapore pork **40**

Hot-smoked trout with beetroot relish **50**

Chunky chilli bean soup **68**

Potato, cucumber & dill salad **84**

Chicken jalfrezi **34**

New potato, bacon & bean salad **44**

4 ProPoints value

Roasted butternut squash soup **66**
♥ GF HC V

4 ProPoints value

Quorn tikka salad **72**
♥ LC V

4 ProPoints value

Tortilla española **76**
♥ GF M V

5 ProPoints value

Beef rogan josh **16**
♥ GF LC

5 ProPoints value

Steak & roast butternut squash salad **18**
♥ GF LC

5 ProPoints value

Caldo verde **36**
♥ GF HC M

5 ProPoints value

Baked potato with Italian tuna topping **62**
♥ GF HC M

5 ProPoints value

Bubble & squeak with poached egg **74**
♥ GF V

6 ProPoints value

Rare beef, watercress & horseradish wraps **12**
♥

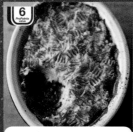
6 ProPoints value

Spiced cottage pie with parsnip mash **22**
♥ GF HC

6 ProPoints value

Mini ham quiches **38**
♥ GF LC

6 ProPoints value

One pan fry-up **46**
♥ GF

6 ProPoints value

Coriander cod with crispy ginger **48**
♥ GF

6 ProPoints value

Sweet roasted veg & cod **54**
♥ GF M

6 ProPoints value

Tuna & bean salad **56**
♥ GF M LC

6 ProPoints value

Prawn & dill open sandwich **64**
♥

6 ProPoints value

Pasta salad with peas & garlicky tomatoes **80**

6 ProPoints value

Toasty porridge with spiced apple compote **86**

7 ProPoints value

Steak with colcannon **20**

7 ProPoints value

One pan harissa chicken **30**

7 ProPoints value

Pork vindaloo-style **42**

7 ProPoints value

Roast vegetable & giant couscous salad **78**

9 ProPoints value

Beef burgers with sweet onion relish & chips **14**

9 ProPoints value

Steak with peppercorn sauce & straw fries **24**

9 ProPoints value

Seared chicken with mint yogurt dressing **32**

10 ProPoints value

Caribbean chicken **26**

10 ProPoints value

Chicken fried rice **28**

10 ProPoints value

Prawn kedgeree **52**

10 ProPoints value

Lemon-marinated salmon with couscous **60**

Rare BEEF, *Watercress* & Horseradish Wraps

 6 *ProPoints* values per serving
ProPoints values per recipe **24**

These tasty wraps are perfect for a weekend lunch, or for a 'grown-up' picnic.

 Serves 4
Preparation time 10 minutes
Cooking time 30–35 minutes

300 g lean beef fillet

calorie controlled cooking spray

1 tablespoon wholegrain mustard

2 teaspoons grated fresh horseradish

75 g quark

4 Weight Watchers tortillas, or similar

50 g pickled beetroot, shredded finely

½ x 85 g bag watercress

freshly ground black pepper

Preheat the oven to Gas Mark 5/190°C/fan oven 170°C. Mist the beef with the cooking spray and heat a frying pan until hot. Cook the beef on all sides for 5 minutes, or until browned.

Brush the beef all over with the mustard, transfer to a baking tray and roast for 25–30 minutes. Leave to cool. Meanwhile, mix the horseradish and quark together and season with black pepper.

Carve the beef into thin slices. Divide the horseradish mixture between the wraps, then top with the beetroot, beef slices and watercress. Roll up the wraps and cut each in half, wrap in baking parchment and tie with string, or serve immediately.

Beef Burgers with Sweet Onion Relish & CHIPS

 ProPoints values per serving
ProPoints values per recipe 34

 Serves 4
Preparation time 10 minutes
 Cooking time 30 minutes

 700 g Maris Piper potatoes, cut
into thick chips
 calorie controlled cooking spray
500 g 5% fat lean beef mince
1 small red onion, grated
2 tablespoons finely chopped fresh
parsley
1 teaspoon Dijon mustard (ensure
gluten free), plus extra to serve
(optional)
salt and freshly ground black
pepper

For the sweet onion relish
2 teaspoons olive oil
1 large onion, sliced finely
1 tablespoon balsamic vinegar

To serve
salad of sliced tomatoes, crisp
lettuce and sliced red onion
cornichons (optional)

A classic burger — but without the bun, so perfect for a Filling & Healthy day or gluten free approach.

Preheat the oven to Gas Mark 7/220°C/fan oven 200°C. Bring a saucepan of water to the boil and add the chips. Bring back to the boil and cook for 5 minutes. Drain well and spread out on a baking sheet. Blot dry with kitchen paper and mist with the cooking spray. Toss to coat then bake for about 30 minutes, or until golden and crispy, turning at least once.

Meanwhile, to make the sweet onion relish, heat the olive oil in a frying pan and add the onion. Cook very gently for around 25 minutes, stirring occasionally, until quite soft and golden. Add the balsamic vinegar, turn the heat up a little, add 1–2 tablespoons of water and cook, stirring, until jammy. Set aside.

Put the mince, grated red onion, parsley and mustard in a bowl. Season and mix together well (it's best to use your hands), then shape into 4 patties. Mist with the cooking spray, then cook in a frying pan for 5–6 minutes, turning occasionally, until done to your liking.

Serve the burgers with the sweet onion relish, chips and salad, plus extra mustard and cornichons, if you like.

> **Cook's tip** The raw burger mixture can be frozen. Simply shape and wrap in cling film and freeze for up to 3 months. Defrost thoroughly in the fridge before cooking.

BEEF
Rogan Josh

 5 ProPoints value

ProPoints values per serving
ProPoints values per recipe 21

 Serves 4
Preparation time 25 minutes
 Cooking time 1 hour

 calorie controlled cooking spray
500 g cubed lean braising steak
 1 large onion, sliced thinly
2 carrots, peeled and sliced
3 garlic cloves, chopped
2.5 cm fresh root ginger, peeled
   and grated
3 cardamom pods, split
1 teaspoon cumin seeds
1 tablespoon medium curry powder
   (ensure gluten free)
2 teaspoons paprika
1 teaspoon mild chilli powder
2 tablespoons tomato purée
300 ml vegetable stock (ensure
   gluten free)
salt and freshly ground black
   pepper

This deliciously rich curry is so easy to make — just chuck it all in the pan and leave it to do its work... 1 hour later and you've got dinner on the table.

Heat a large, heavy based, lidded saucepan over a medium heat. Spray with the cooking spray and cook the beef for 6 minutes until browned all over. Remove the beef and any juices from the pan, then set aside.

Add the onion and carrots to the pan and spray with more cooking spray, stir and cover. Cook the onion and carrots for 5 minutes over a medium heat until softened. Stir occasionally. Add the garlic, ginger, cardamom, cumin seeds, curry powder, paprika, chilli powder and tomato purée and stir to coat the vegetables in the spices.

Return the beef, and any juices, to the pan with the stock and bring to the boil, then reduce the heat to low and part-cover. Simmer gently, stirring occasionally, for 1 hour or until the beef is tender. Season before serving.

STEAK & Roast Butternut *Squash* Salad

5 ProPoints value

ProPoints values per serving
ProPoints values per recipe 9

Serves 2
Preparation time 5 minutes
Cooking time 25 minutes

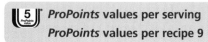

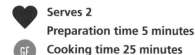

350 g butternut squash, peeled
    and cut into bite-size pieces
5 small shallots, peeled and halved
a pinch of dried red chilli flakes
2 x 100 g lean sirloin steaks
1½ teaspoons olive oil
salt and freshly ground black
    pepper

For the salad
100 g mixed salad leaves
½ teaspoon extra virgin olive oil
juice of ½ small lemon

The seared steak goes really well with the roasted vegetables in this salad, which is perfect if you're also following a gluten free or lower carb approach.

Preheat the oven to Gas Mark 6/200°C/fan oven 180°C. Place the squash and shallots in a roasting tray, season and sprinkle with the chilli flakes. Rub the steaks with a little of the olive oil and set aside. Drizzle the rest of the oil over the vegetables and roast them for 25 minutes, or until soft and starting to char.

When the vegetables are nearly ready, heat a small non-stick frying pan and add the steaks. Sear for 2–3 minutes on each side, or until done to your liking. Place on a plate, season and leave to rest for a few minutes.

Place the mixed leaves in a serving bowl, season and toss with the extra virgin olive oil and lemon juice. Slice the steak into strips, and serve straightaway with the salad, along with the squash and shallots.

STEAK with
Colcannon

 7 *ProPoints* values per serving
ProPoints values per recipe 29

 Serves 4
Takes 25 minutes

425 g potatoes, peeled and cut
into chunks
150 g sweetheart cabbage or kale,
shredded finely
1 leek, sliced thinly
6 spring onions, sliced thinly
calorie controlled cooking spray
4 x 140 g lean fillet steaks
salt and freshly ground black
pepper
fresh coriander sprigs, to garnish
(optional)

Colcannon is a traditional mash flavoured with spring onions, cabbage and leek and it goes particularly well with pan-fried steak. If you have time, remove the steak from the fridge at least half an hour before cooking to allow it to come up to room temperature — this will help the meat cook evenly.

Put the potatoes in a medium lidded saucepan and cover with water. Bring to the boil and simmer for about 10 minutes or until tender. Drain and return to the pan, then place briefly on the turned-off hot hob to allow the potatoes to dry out slightly. Season the potatoes and mash until smooth.

Meanwhile, put the cabbage, leek and spring onions in another medium lidded saucepan, spray with the cooking spray, and add 1 tablespoon of water. Cook over a medium heat, covered, for 5 minutes or until tender, stirring regularly. Stir the vegetables into the mash until combined, then cover to keep warm.

Spray each side of the steaks with the cooking spray and season. Heat a griddle or large, non-stick frying pan and cook the steaks two at a time for 2 minutes on each side, turning every minute, or until cooked to your liking. Cover the first two with foil to keep warm while you cook the second two.

Spoon the mash on to 4 plates and serve with the steak, drizzling over any juices from the pan. Garnish with the coriander, if using.

Variation
Colcannon also goes really well with a 140 g **lean gammon steak** per person for the same *ProPoints* values per serving. Cook two steaks at a time for 3–4 minutes on each side. Cover the first batch with foil to keep warm while you cook the second batch.

Spiced COTTAGE PIE with Parsnip Mash

 ProPoints values per serving
ProPoints values per recipe 25

Serves 4
Preparation time 55 minutes
Cooking time 20 minutes

calorie controlled cooking spray
2 onions, chopped
2 carrots, peeled and grated coarsely
1 celery stick, chopped finely
125g mushrooms, sliced thinly
3 garlic cloves, chopped
300 g 5% fat lean beef mince
1 tablespoon mild curry powder (ensure gluten free)
1 tablespoon tomato purée
100 g frozen petits pois
1 beef stock cube (ensure gluten free)
300 ml hot water
325 g potatoes, peeled and cut into even-sized chunks
275 g parsnips, peeled and cut into even-sized chunks
salt and freshly ground black pepper

A twist on the classic dish with the addition of spices in the mince base and parsnips in the mash. And not only is it great for when you're on a Filling & Healthy day approach, but it's perfect if you're following a gluten free diet as well.

Heat a large, non-stick, lidded saucepan over a medium heat and spray with the cooking spray. Cook the onions, covered, for 6 minutes until softened. Add the carrots, celery, mushrooms and garlic, spray again, and cook for another 5 minutes, until softened.

Meanwhile, heat a large lidded non-stick frying pan over a medium heat, and add the mince, curry powder and tomato purée. Bring to a simmer then reduce the heat to low and cook, part-covered, for 10 minutes, stirring occasionally. Add the petits pois, stir and replace the lid, then cook for another 5 minutes until browned all over, stirring to break up any lumps of meat. Dissolve the stock cube in the water and pour into the pan with the vegetables. Add the mince mixture. Bring to the boil, then reduce the heat to low and simmer, part-covered, for 15 minutes, then season.

Preheat the oven to Gas Mark 4/180°C/fan oven 160°C. Meanwhile, place the potatoes and parsnips in a medium lidded saucepan and cover with water. Bring to the boil and simmer for 10–15 minutes until tender. Drain and return to the pan then place on the turned-off hot hob to let them dry slightly. Season and mash the potatoes and parsnips until smooth.

Put the mince mixture into a 1.7 litre deep ovenproof dish and top with the mash – you want the top to be quite rough so that it browns nicely. Cook in the oven for 20 minutes until the top is golden.

> **Cook's tip** Cottage pie freezes well: try freezing individual portions before baking. They will freeze for up to 1 month. Make sure you defrost thoroughly before cooking.

STEAK with Peppercorn Sauce & Straw Fries

 9 *ProPoints* values per serving
ProPoints values per recipe 17

 Serves 2
Takes 30 minutes

300 g potatoes, peeled and cut
    into thin chips
calorie controlled cooking spray
2 x 110 g thin cut lean sirloin steaks
salt
150 g trimmed green beans
1 tablespoon wholegrain mustard
    (ensure gluten free), to serve

For the sauce
50 ml hot beef stock (ensure
    gluten free)
2 teaspoons roughly crushed
    peppercorns
2 tablespoons quark

**Succulent steak and crispy fries — what could be better?
Some fresh green beans add the finishing touch.**

Preheat the oven to Gas Mark 7/220°C/fan oven 200°C. Bring a saucepan of water to the boil and add the chips. Bring back to the boil and cook for 3 minutes. Drain well and spread out on a baking sheet. Blot dry with kitchen paper and mist with the cooking spray. Toss to coat then bake for 20–25 minutes until golden and crispy, turning at least once.

Meanwhile, to make the sauce, bring the stock and peppercorns to the boil in a small pan. Simmer gently for a minute or two then remove from the heat and stir in the quark. Keep warm.

Season the steaks with a little salt. Heat a non-stick frying pan or griddle pan until hot and cook for 3–4 minutes, turning once.

Bring a small saucepan of water to the boil, add the beans and cook for 3 minutes until tender. Drain and serve with the steak and chips, with some sauce drizzled over and mustard on the side.

Caribbean Chicken

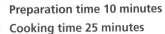
 Serves 2
Preparation time 10 minutes
 Cooking time 25 minutes

 2 x 165 g skinless chicken breasts, scored

 90 g long grain dried brown rice

juice of ½ lime, plus wedges to serve

½ small packet fresh coriander, chopped

calorie controlled cooking spray

1 red pepper, de-seeded and diced

1 ripe mango, diced

3 spring onions, sliced finely

1 red chilli, de-seeded and sliced

salt and freshly ground black pepper

For the jerk seasoning

2 teaspoons olive oil

1 teaspoon ground allspice

½ teaspoon dried red chilli flakes

¼ teaspoon dried thyme

¼ teaspoon smoked paprika

¼ teaspoon ground mixed spice

¼ teaspoon garlic granules

This jerk chicken recipe is made from scratch so you can really appreciate the flavours coming through; and the fresh mango gives it a really authentic taste.

Combine the jerk seasoning ingredients with a little salt and plenty of black pepper and rub all over the chicken. Set aside.

Cook the rice following the packet instructions, then drain, and stir through the lime juice, coriander and some seasoning. Keep warm.

Meanwhile, heat a non-stick frying pan and mist it with the cooking spray. Add the red pepper and cook for 5 minutes to soften without it colouring too much (you may need to add a splash of water). Add the mango, spring onions and chilli, and another splash of water. Season and simmer for 5–10 minutes, or until sweet and soft with no excess water.

While the rice and vegetables are cooking, heat a non-stick frying pan or griddle pan, then cook the chicken for 12–15 minutes, turning often, so that it is charred on the outside and cooked through and juicy on the inside. Leave to rest for a few minutes then slice. Serve with the rice and vegetables, and the lime wedges to squeeze over.

Chicken *Fried* RICE

ProPoints values per serving **10**
ProPoints values per recipe 41

Serves 4
Preparation time 10 minutes

Cooking time 15 minutes

4 teaspoons sunflower oil
400 g skinless chicken breast, sliced
15 g fresh root ginger, peeled and
   chopped finely
2 garlic cloves, chopped
4 spring onions, sliced finely
400 g cooked brown rice
100 g peas, defrosted if frozen
100 g sweetcorn, defrosted if frozen
2 eggs
1 tablespoon reduced salt soy sauce
   (ensure gluten free)
a handful of fresh coriander
freshly ground black pepper

This quick and easy stir-fry makes a great midweek supper.

Heat a wok or non-stick frying pan, add 1 teaspoon of the oil and half the chicken, and stir-fry for 3–4 minutes, or until cooked. Set aside and season with black pepper. Repeat with another teaspoon of oil and the rest of the chicken.

Turn down the heat, add the remaining oil to the wok along with the ginger, garlic and spring onions. Stir-fry for 1–2 minutes, then add the rice, peas and sweetcorn and heat through. Make a well in the middle and crack in 1 of the eggs. Gradually work it into the rice mixture, then repeat with the second egg. Stir in the chicken and soy sauce to warm through, then sprinkle with the coriander and serve.

One Pan
Harissa CHICKEN

 7 *ProPoints* values per serving
ProPoints values per recipe 14

 Serves 2
Preparation time 5 minutes
 Cooking time 20–25 minutes

1 red onion, cut into thin wedges
1 red pepper, chopped
150 g butternut squash, peeled and diced
1 courgette, cut into small chunks
2 x 165 g skinless chicken breasts
300 ml hot chicken stock
2 teaspoons harissa paste
50 g giant wholewheat couscous
2 tablespoons chopped fresh parsley

So simple to prepare, this Moroccan-inspired one-pot dish is a winner every time.

Preheat the oven to Gas Mark 6/200°C/fan oven 180°C. Place all the vegetables in a roasting tin and sit the chicken breasts on top. Pour over half the stock. Spread the harissa over the chicken and roast for 20–25 minutes until the chicken and vegetables are cooked through.

Meanwhile, put the couscous in the remaining hot stock, cover and leave to soak for 5 minutes. Fluff up the couscous using a fork and add to the roasting tin, pushing it down into the liquid for the final 5 minutes in the oven. Serve garnished with the parsley.

Seared Chicken with Mint YOGURT Dressing

 9 ProPoints values per serving
ProPoints values per recipe 17

 Serves 2
Takes 25 minutes

75 g dried wholewheat couscous
½ teaspoon vegetable stock powder
   or ½ stock cube
300 g skinless boneless chicken
   breast, cut into 1 cm wide strips
2 teaspoons dried thyme
2 teaspoons ground coriander
calorie controlled cooking spray
50 g frozen peas
50 g sugar snap peas, sliced
   diagonally
½ red pepper, de-seeded and cut
   into thin strips
1 large spring onion, sliced
   diagonally
salt and freshly ground black
   pepper

For the mint yogurt dressing
a small handful of fresh mint leaves
75 g 0% fat natural Greek yogurt
juice of ½ lime
½ teaspoon cumin seeds

Couscous is a staple food in North African cuisine and is usually served with a stew spooned over it. Here, the mint yogurt dressing, chicken strips and delicious fresh veg do the job of the stew.

Put the couscous in a bowl, pour over enough boiling water to cover, stir in the stock powder or crumbled stock cube and cover with a plate. Leave for about 5 minutes or until the stock is absorbed and the grains are tender. Using a fork, fluff up the couscous and set aside.

Meanwhile, using a hand-held blender, blend together all the dressing ingredients, except the cumin seeds. If you don't have a hand-held blender, finely chop the mint and combine with the yogurt and lime juice. Transfer to a bowl, season and scatter over the cumin seeds.

Sprinkle the chicken with the thyme and coriander. Season then turn until evenly coated. Heat a griddle pan or non-stick frying pan over a high heat. Spray the chicken with the cooking spray. Cook over a medium-high heat for 6 minutes, turning once, until cooked through and golden.

Meanwhile, bring a saucepan of water to the boil, add the peas, sugar snaps, pepper and spring onion and cook for 3 minutes, or until tender. Drain and refresh under cold running water.

Divide the couscous between 2 large, shallow bowls then top with the peas, sugar snaps, pepper, spring onion and chicken. Serve with the dressing spooned over.

 Variation
Swap the chicken for 2 x 40 g slices of light halloumi per person for 8 *ProPoints* values per serving. Pat dry with kitchen towel and prepare in the same way as the chicken, then griddle or pan fry for 2 minutes on each side or until golden.

Chicken JALFREZI

 4 *ProPoints* values per serving
ProPoints values per recipe 16

* Serves 4
Takes 40 minutes

♥

 GF

 LC

calorie controlled cooking spray
2 onions, chopped
1 red pepper, de-seeded and sliced
2 garlic cloves, crushed
5 cm fresh root ginger, grated (no need to peel)
600 g skinless boneless chicken breasts, cubed
1 green pepper, de-seeded and sliced
1 green chilli, de-seeded and sliced thinly into rounds
1 tablespoon medium curry powder (ensure gluten free)
1 teaspoon cumin seeds
400 g passata
salt and freshly ground black pepper

Jalfrezi curries are cooked quickly, in a similar way to a stir-fry, so the chicken needs to be cut into small, equal-sized pieces so that it cooks speedily and evenly.

Heat a lidded saucepan over a medium heat. Spray with the cooking spray and fry the onions for 5 minutes. Add the red pepper, garlic and ginger, spray again with the cooking spray, and fry for another 3 minutes until the vegetables have softened.

Using a hand-held blender, purée the onion mixture with 4 tablespoons of water until smooth, then remove the onion mixture from the pan and set to one side until ready to use.

Return the pan to the heat, spray with the cooking spray, and stir-fry the chicken for 5 minutes until browned in places. Add the green pepper and chilli, then stir-fry for another 2 minutes.

Return the onion mixture to the pan and add the curry powder, cumin seeds and passata. Stir, bring to the boil, then reduce the heat and simmer, part-covered, for 10 minutes, until the sauce has reduced and thickened and the chicken has cooked through. Season and serve.

Variation

If you're following a higher carb approach, serve with 60 g dried wild or **brown rice** per person, cooked following the packet instructions, for an extra 6 *ProPoints* values per serving.

Caldo verde

 5 *ProPoints* values per serving
ProPoints values per recipe 19

  Serves 4
Preparation time 15 minutes
 Cooking time 25 minutes

 2 teaspoons extra virgin olive oil
1 large onion, diced
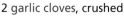 4 bacon medallions, chopped
2 garlic cloves, crushed
 ½ teaspoon smoked paprika
1.2 litres chicken stock made using
   2 cubes (ensure gluten free)
400 g potatoes, chopped
400 g can haricot or flageolet
   beans, drained and rinsed
150 g Savoy cabbage, kale or spring
   greens, shredded

A traditional Portuguese soup, Caldo Verde is hearty and warming, and makes for a meal in itself.

Heat 1 teaspoon of the oil in a large saucepan. Add the onion and fry for 5 minutes, or until softened. Add the bacon, garlic and paprika and a splash of the stock. Cook, stirring, for 2 minutes.

Add the remaining stock and the potatoes. Cover, bring to the boil and simmer for 15 minutes until the potatoes are tender.

Add the beans and cabbage. Simmer, uncovered, for 2 minutes, or until everything is heated through.

Serve drizzled with the remaining oil.

Mini Ham QUICHES

 6 *ProPoints* values per serving
ProPoints values per recipe 13

 Serves 2
Preparation time 10 minutes
Cooking time 15 minutes

 calorie controlled cooking spray
8 x 15 g premium ham slices
4 eggs
3 tablespoons skimmed milk
4 fresh chive stalks
salt and freshly ground black
      pepper

These clever pastry-free quiches are perfect for when you're on a Filling & Healthy day approach, or if you're going gluten free for that matter.

Preheat the oven to Gas Mark 5/190°C/fan oven 170°C. Spray four holes of a deep muffin tin with the cooking spray. Stack two slices of ham on top of each other, then gather up the edges and pop into one of the holes in the muffin tray. Press the ham down to make a 'case' – it doesn't matter if it gathers slightly in places. Repeat with the remaining ham to fill four holes.

In a jug beat together the eggs and milk and season with a little salt and a generous amount of pepper. Pour the mixture carefully into the ham cases until it almost comes to the top. Snip over the chives.

Bake the quiches for about 15 minutes until the filling is just firm. Leave to cool in the tin, then ease out each quiche using a knife. Serve two quiches per person.

> **Cook's tip** If taking these quiches for a packed lunch or picnic, be sure to wrap them carefully in foil so they survive the journey intact.

Singapore Pork

 3 *ProPoints* values per serving
ProPoints values per recipe 13

This simple weekday meal uses lots of fresh vegetables and can be rustled up in a matter of minutes.

♥ **Serves 4**
Takes 25 minutes

 GF

 LC

400 g pork tenderloin, visible fat
   removed, cut into strips
4 tablespoons dark soy sauce
   (ensure gluten free)
calorie controlled cooking spray
1 onion, sliced thinly
75 g baby corn, halved lengthways
1 yellow pepper, de-seeded and
   cut into strips
100 g mange tout, halved
   diagonally
1 red chilli, de-seeded and cut
   into rounds
1 teaspoon ground turmeric
2 teaspoons artificial sweetener
   (or to taste)
juice of 1 lime
50 g beansprouts

Put the pork and soy sauce in a shallow dish and turn until the meat is coated. Set aside.

Heat a wok or large non-stick frying pan. Spray with the cooking spray and stir-fry the onion and baby corn for 3 minutes. Add the yellow pepper and mange tout and stir-fry for another minute. Transfer to a bowl while you cook the pork.

Remove the pork from the soy sauce and add to the pan. Spray with the cooking spray and stir-fry for 3 minutes. Stir the chilli, turmeric, sweetener and lime juice into the soy sauce. Add to the pan, and stir-fry for 1 minute.

Return the vegetables to the pan and add the beansprouts. Stir briefly until combined, then serve immediately .

 Variation

You can use 350 g **meat-free pieces** instead of the pork in this recipe for a ***ProPoints*** value of 3 per serving. Prepare and cook in the same way as the pork. However, be aware that meat free pieces are not gluten free.

Pork *Vindaloo* -Style

7 *ProPoints* values per serving
ProPoints values per recipe 14

Serves 2
Takes 20 minutes

calorie controlled cooking spray
250 g lean pork loin steak, cut into thin strips
1 onion, sliced thinly
1 red pepper, de-seeded and sliced
3 garlic cloves, chopped
2.5 cm fresh root ginger, peeled and sliced very thinly
1 teaspoon cumin seeds
1 teaspoon ground coriander
½ teaspoon turmeric
2 teaspoons tomato purée
a pinch of artificial sweetener (or to taste)
2 teaspoons white wine vinegar
½ vegetable stock cube (ensure gluten free)
¼–½ teaspoon dried chilli flakes
freshly ground black pepper

To serve
1 tablespoon roughly chopped fresh coriander
2 tablespoons low fat natural yogurt

This tasty curry has all the flavours of a traditional vindaloo, but without being overwhelmingly hot and, as an added bonus, it's also much quicker to make. If you're following a higher carb approach, serve with 40 g dried brown basmati rice per person, cooked following the packet instructions, for an extra 4 *ProPoints* values per serving.

Heat a wok or large non-stick frying pan over a high heat. Spray with the cooking spray, add the pork, and cook for 2 minutes until starting to brown. Turn the pork and cook for another 2 minutes until cooked through. Transfer the pork and any liquid in the wok to a plate and set aside until needed.

Reduce the heat slightly, spray with more cooking spray and add the onion to the wok or pan. Stir-fry for 1 minute, then add the red pepper, garlic and ginger and stir-fry for a further minute.

Add the cumin seeds, ground coriander, turmeric, tomato purée, sweetener, vinegar, stock cube and chilli flakes, then return the pork to the wok. Stir-fry for another minute and season with black pepper. Sprinkle with the fresh coriander and serve with 1 tablespoon of yogurt per person.

New Potato, *Bacon* & BEAN SALAD

 4 *ProPoints* values per serving
ProPoints values per recipe 18

 Serves 4
Takes 25 minutes

400 g new potatoes, scrubbed
  and quartered
200 g frozen sliced runner beans
100 g frozen peas
calorie controlled cooking spray
4 unsmoked bacon medallions,
  chopped
200 g mixed salad leaves
150 g cherry tomatoes, halved

For the dressing
2 teaspoons cider vinegar
1 tablespoon extra virgin olive oil
2 teaspoons wholegrain mustard
  (ensure gluten free)
1 garlic clove, crushed
salt and freshly ground black
  pepper

Enjoy the taste of summer all year round with this fresh, hearty salad.

Boil the potatoes for 15 minutes, adding the runner beans and peas for the final 2 minutes. Drain well. To make the dressing, mix together the cider vinegar, olive oil, mustard and garlic. Season and set aside.

Meanwhile, mist a frying pan with the cooking spray and place it over a medium heat. Add the chopped bacon and fry, stirring, for 3–4 minutes, or until browned and crisp.

Place the warm potatoes, beans, peas and bacon in a large bowl with the salad leaves and tomatoes. Drizzle the dressing over and toss to mix. Divide between 4 warm plates and serve.

One Pan
Fry-up

 6 *ProPoints* values per serving
ProPoints values per recipe 11

 Serves 2
Takes 20 minutes

 calorie controlled cooking spray
250 g potatoes, peeled and cut
    into 2 cm dice
3 bacon medallions, chopped
150 g chestnut or button
    mushrooms, sliced thickly
2 eggs
freshly ground black pepper

A scrumptious brunch dish for sharing on a lazy weekend, with just one pan to wash up afterwards. Relax and enjoy alongside the weekend papers.

Spray a lidded non-stick frying pan lightly with the cooking spray. Stir-fry the potatoes for 3–4 minutes over a high heat until starting to brown at the edges. Season with pepper, add 3 tablespoons of water and cover the pan. Cook, covered, for 5 minutes over a lowish heat, stirring once or twice, until the potatoes are almost cooked through.

Remove the lid, add the bacon and increase the heat under the pan to medium. Cook for 2 minutes, then add the mushrooms and cook for a further 2–3 minutes.

Make two spaces in the potato mixture and break an egg into each gap. Cover the pan again and cook gently for 2 minutes or until the eggs are cooked to your liking. Serve on warmed plates.

 Variation

Replace the bacon with 50 g meat-free bacon-style rashers, chopped. They need less cooking than bacon, so add them to the potato and mushroom mixture just before adding the eggs to the pan. The *ProPoints* values will be 5 per serving.

Cook's tip If your frying pan doesn't have a lid you can improvise with a baking tray or a large plate placed on top – but make sure that you use oven gloves to lift it off as it will get hot.

Coriander Cod with CRISPY Ginger

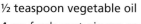 **6** *ProPoints* values per serving
ProPoints values per recipe 11

 Serves 2
Takes 25 minutes

 GF

calorie controlled cooking spray
½ teaspoon vegetable oil
4 cm fresh root ginger, peeled
   and cut into matchsticks
2 x 200 g thick cod fillets
2 large garlic cloves, crushed
1 teaspoon ground coriander
½ teaspoon turmeric
½ teaspoon ground cumin
4 tablespoons low fat natural
   yogurt
1 tablespoon lemon juice
2 tablespoons chopped fresh
   coriander
salt and freshly ground black
   pepper

Full of vibrant flavours thanks to the herbs, ginger and spices, this light fish dish is delicious served with spinach and 40 g dried brown rice per person, cooked following the packet instructions, for an extra 4 *ProPoints* values per serving.

Preheat the grill to high and line the grill pan with foil. Spray a non-stick frying pan with the cooking spray and add the oil. Add the ginger and fry for 3–5 minutes, stirring occasionally, until light golden and crisp. Drain on kitchen towel and set to one side.

Season the fish and grill for 8–10 minutes, turning once, until cooked.

While the fish is grilling, spray the frying pan that you used for the ginger with the cooking spray. Fry the garlic for 30 seconds, then stir in the spices. Turn the heat to low, add 3 tablespoons of water, the yogurt and lemon juice. Stir until combined and gently heat through for 2 minutes or until reduced and slightly thickened. Add half of the fresh coriander and season.

Place the fish on 2 plates and pour any juices from the grilled fish into the yogurt sauce. Stir the sauce, then spoon it over the fish and scatter over the crispy ginger and the remaining coriander, then serve.

HOT-SMOKED Trout
with *Beetroot Relish*

3 *ProPoints* values per serving
ProPoints values per recipe 5

Serves 2
Takes 10 minutes

2 x 65 g cooked hot-smoked
 trout fillets
½ teaspoon cumin seeds

For the beetroot relish
150 g cooked beetroot, diced
2 tablespoons fat-free natural
 yogurt
2 teaspoons lemon juice
1 garlic clove, crushed
salt and freshly ground black
 pepper

If you're following a higher carb approach, serve the trout and relish with 100 g boiled new potatoes and a large handful of watercress per person for an extra 2 *ProPoints* values per serving.

To make the beetroot relish, mix together the beetroot, yogurt, lemon juice and garlic in a bowl. (You can also purée the beetroot mixture using a hand-held blender, if you prefer a smooth relish.) Season.

Put a trout fillet on each serving plate, or flake it into pieces, and serve with the beetroot relish. Sprinkle the cumin seeds over the top.

Variation
The same amount of smoked salmon would make a delicious alternative to the hot-smoked trout, for the same *ProPoints* values per serving.

Cook's tip The beetroot relish will keep, covered, in the fridge for up to 3 days. Sprinkle the cumin seeds over just before serving.

Prawn KEDGEREE

10 *ProPoints* values per serving
ProPoints values per recipe 19

Serves 2
Takes 40 minutes

4 teaspoons mild curry powder
(ensure gluten free)
juice of ½ lemon
125 g frozen, peeled, raw king
prawns, defrosted
100 g dried brown basmati rice,
washed
2 eggs
calorie controlled cooking spray
1 large onion, diced
2 large garlic cloves, chopped
75 g frozen petits pois
½ vegetable stock cube (ensure
gluten free)
1 tablespoon chopped fresh parsley,
to garnish (optional)

This is a traditional British breakfast from colonial India, but it also makes a delicious lunch or supper dish. Although kedgeree normally includes smoked fish, this version features prawns for a delicious alternative.

In a bowl, mix together 1 teaspoon of the curry powder with 1 teaspoon of the lemon juice. Pat the prawns dry with kitchen towel and add to the marinade, then turn until coated. Marinate, covered, in the fridge until ready to use, but not more than 1 hour.

Bring a large saucepan of water to the boil and cook the rice following the packet instructions, then drain and rinse under cold running water and leave to drain until ready to use. Meanwhile, hard-boil the eggs then cool them briefly under cold running water. Peel and quarter the eggs, and set aside.

Heat a large, non-stick, lidded frying pan over a medium heat and spray with the cooking spray. Cook the onion, covered, for 6 minutes, adding a splash of water if it becomes very dry. Add the garlic and cook, covered, for another 2 minutes. Add the petits pois and cook for 2 more minutes, stirring until softened. Stir in the remaining curry powder and lemon juice, the stock cube and cooked rice, and mix well until combined. Cover and heat through for a couple of minutes. Remove from the heat and set aside, covered, while you cook the prawns.

Heat a wok or non-stick frying pan over a high heat. Spray with the cooking spray and stir-fry the prawns for 2 minutes until pink and cooked through. Spoon the rice on to 2 plates, top with the prawns and egg quarters. Scatter the parsley over the top, if using.

 Variation

For a vegetarian version, swap the prawns for 125 g meat-free chicken-style pieces. Coat in the spices and add to the pan with the onion, for 10 *ProPoints* values per serving.

Sweet Roasted Veg & COD

 6 *ProPoints* values per serving
ProPoints values per recipe 24

 Serves 4
Preparation time 10 minutes
 Cooking time 55–70 minutes

 GF
 M

400 g butternut squash, peeled
and chopped
300 g sweet potatoes, diced
(no need to peel)
1 large red pepper, de-seeded and
cut into chunks
1 large red onion, cut into wedges
8 garlic cloves in their skins
4 teaspoons olive oil
a few sprigs of woody fresh herbs,
such as thyme, oregano or
rosemary
4 x 150 g cod loin fillets
1 lemon, sliced, plus wedges to
serve
salt and freshly ground black
pepper
a handful of chopped fresh flat leaf
parsley, to serve

This chunky cod and roasted veg combo has the vibrant colours and flavours of the sunny Mediterranean. Serve with a green salad, for no additional *ProPoints* values.

Preheat the oven to Gas Mark 6/200°C/fan oven 180°C. Put the vegetables in a roasting tin, season well, drizzle over 3 teaspoons of the olive oil and add the woody herbs. Toss everything together to coat in the oil, then roast for 40–50 minutes, or until everything is tender.

Once the vegetables are cooked, add the cod on top and lay 2–3 slices of lemon over each piece. Season lightly and return to the oven for another 15–20 minutes, or until the fish is opaque and comes away in large flakes when parted with a fork. Drizzle the fish with the remaining teaspoon of oil, scatter the parsley over, then serve with lemon wedges to squeeze over.

Cook's tip If you're following a higher carb approach, add 300 g parboiled halved new potatoes to the tin at the start of cooking for an extra 2 *ProPoints* values per person.

Tuna & BEAN Salad

6 *Propoints* values per serving
ProPoints values per recipe 13

A fresh-tasting twist on the Italian classic, this salad is packed full of goodness and great for lunch or a light dinner.

Serves 2

Takes 20 minutes

½ teaspoon cumin seeds

¼ garlic clove

2 teaspoons extra virgin olive oil

1 tablespoon lemon juice

200 g canned haricot beans, drained and rinsed

1 tablespoon finely chopped fresh parsley

2 eggs

80 g green beans, trimmed and halved

100 g (2–3 small) vacuum-packed beetroot, cut into chunks

1 head romaine lettuce, roughly torn

185 g can tuna in spring water, drained

salt and freshly ground black pepper

Toast the cumin seeds in a dry frying pan for around 1 minute, or until fragrant. Tip into a mortar and bash together with the garlic. Blend with the oil and lemon juice, then stir into the haricot beans with the parsley and some seasoning and set aside to let the flavours mingle – the longer the better.

Hard-boil the eggs, adding the green beans to the pan for the last 2 minutes of cooking. Drain and add the green beans to the haricot bean mixture. Cool the eggs under cold running water, then peel and halve them, and set aside.

Toss the beetroot, lettuce and tuna through the beans, then top with the halved eggs and serve.

CHILLI LIME *Salmon & Prawn* Skewers

 2 *Propoints* values per serving
ProPoints values per recipe 12

❤ **Serves 6**
Takes 15 minutes + marinating

zest and juice of 1 lime, plus wedges
    to serve
½ red chilli, de-seeded and chopped
    finely
200 g cooked skinless salmon fillet,
    chopped into 2 cm cubes (approx.
    18 cubes)
12 large cooked peeled king prawns
150 g mango, chopped into 2 cm
    cubes
salt

A fabulous low *ProPoints* value starter or barbie addition, with a hint of the exotic.

Put the lime zest and juice in a large non-metallic bowl. Add the chilli and a good pinch of salt. Stir well.

Add the salmon and prawns and turn to coat. Cover and chill for at least 1 hour and up to 4 hours.

Drain and discard the marinade. Thread 1 or 2 cubes of salmon on to a skewer with a prawn and a piece of mango. Repeat with the remaining ingredients until you have 12 skewers.

Serve 2 skewers per person, with lime wedges to squeeze over.

Variation
Try papaya instead of mango if you like. The *ProPoints* values will be the same.

Lemon-Marinated SALMON with *Couscous*

10 *ProPoints* values per serving
ProPoints values per recipe 40

Serves 4
Takes 25 minutes

4 x 125 g skinless salmon fillets
zest and juice of 1 lemon
160 g dried wholewheat couscous
2 ripe tomatoes, sliced into wedges
4 cm piece of cucumber, de-seeded
  and thinly sliced
a small handful of fresh coriander
  leaves, chopped roughly
½ small red onion, sliced thinly
1 teaspoon extra virgin olive oil
salt and freshly ground black
  pepper

This delicious grilled salmon dish makes an ideal weekend supper to impress.

Put the salmon fillets in a large shallow bowl and drizzle most of the lemon juice over. Leave to marinate for 5 minutes.

Preheat the grill to medium and line the grill pan with foil. Grill the salmon, turning occasionally, for 8–10 minutes, or until the fillets are just cooked through.

Meanwhile, cook the couscous following the packet instructions. Fluff it up with a fork, season and add the lemon zest, remaining lemon juice and other ingredients. Serve one salmon fillet per person, with the couscous salad.

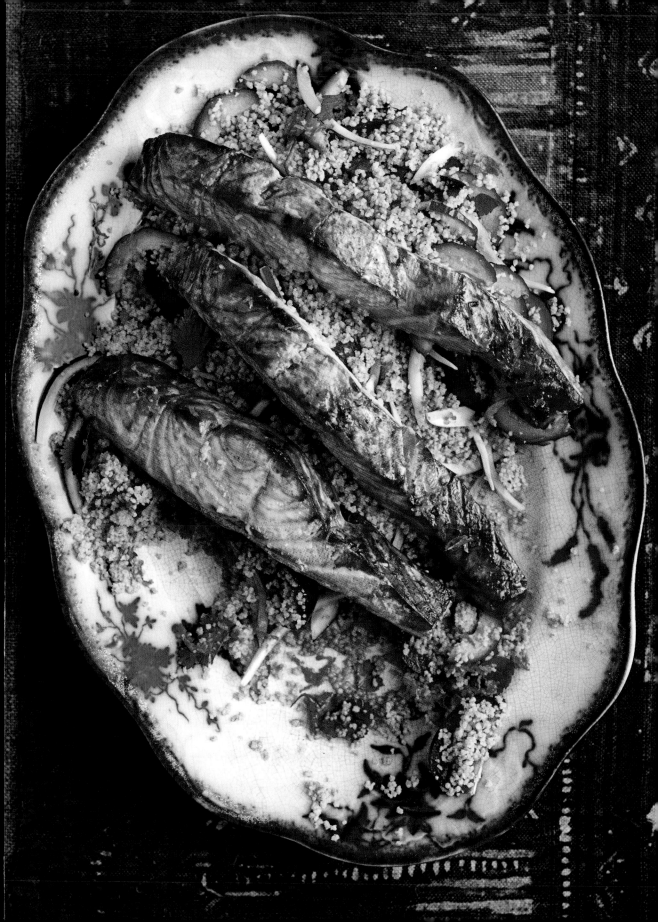

BAKED POTATO with *Italian* Tuna Topping

5 *ProPoints* values per serving
ProPoints values per recipe 5

Serves 1
Preparation time 5 minutes

 Cooking time 1 hour

150 g baking potato
80 g can tuna in spring water,
   drained

25 g quark
1 heaped teaspoon drained capers
1 heaped teaspoon chopped red
   onion
1 heaped teaspoon chopped fresh
   parsley
zest of ½ small lemon
salt and freshly ground black
   pepper
mixed salad leaves and tomato
   halves, to serve

The capers and red onion make a nice change from the normal tuna mayo option.

Preheat the oven to Gas Mark 5/190°C/fan oven 170°C. Bake the potato for 1 hour, or until tender – times vary. (But, if you're in a hurry, it will take around 10 minutes in a microwave.)

In a bowl, mix together the tuna, quark, capers, onion, parsley and lemon zest, and season. Split the potato and pile the tuna on top. Serve with a salad of mixed leaves and tomato halves.

Cook's tip Stir ½ teaspoon extra virgin olive oil from your healthy oil allowance into the mix to really bring the flavours together. This will add 1 extra *ProPoints* value to the recipe.

Prawn & DILL
Open Sandwich

6 *ProPoints* values per serving
ProPoints values per recipe 6

Serves 1
Takes 5 minutes

1 brown sandwich thin, **halved**
100 g low fat natural cottage
    cheese
fresh dill **sprig**
Tabasco sauce (optional)
thinly sliced cucumber
60 g cooked peeled large prawns
freshly ground black pepper

These super-quick open sandwiches make an ideal light snack or simple lunch.

Lightly toast the sandwich thin halves. Mix the cottage cheese with some snipped dill, a few drops of Tabasco, if using, and some black pepper. Pile the mixture on top of the sandwich thins, then add the cucumber slices, prawns, another sprinkling of dill and splash of Tabasco and serve.

Roasted Butternut SQUASH Soup

ProPoints values per serving
ProPoints values per recipe 25

Serves 6
Preparation time 15 minutes
Cooking time 45 minutes

1 red onion, chopped

1 garlic clove, halved

1 fresh rosemary sprig, leaves only, reserving a little for garnish

800 g butternut squash, peeled, de-seeded and cut into small chunks

2 carrots, peeled and chopped roughly

½ swede, peeled and chopped roughly

calorie controlled cooking spray

1 litre boiling water

salt and freshly ground black pepper

6 x 60 g wholemeal bread rolls (ensure gluten free), to serve

By cooking the vegetables in the oven, you intensify their flavour and bring out their natural sweetness.

Preheat the oven to Gas Mark 5/190°C/fan oven 170°C. Put the onion, garlic, rosemary, squash, carrots and swede on a large non-stick baking tray and spray generously with the cooking spray. Roast in the oven for 45 minutes until golden and tender, stirring halfway through.

Transfer the vegetables to a blender and whizz in batches with a little of the boiling water until smooth. Transfer the purée to a large saucepan and add the remaining water. Or, using a hand-held blender, whizz the vegetables with all the water in a large pan until smooth. Gently heat the soup until just before boiling and check the seasoning. Garnish with the reserved rosemary leaves, chopped, and a sprinkling of black pepper, and serve with a bread roll.

Cook's tip If freezing, divide the soup equally between foil trays or containers. Leave to cool completely. Seal, label and freeze for up to 3 months. To serve, defrost the soup then put in a saucepan and reheat on a low heat for 5–7 minutes until piping hot, stirring occasionally. Or microwave on high for 4 minutes, stirring halfway through. Leave to stand for 1 minute before serving.

Chunky CHILLI Bean Soup

 3 *ProPoints* values per serving
ProPoints values per recipe **15**

✱ **Serves 6**
Takes 30 minutes

♥ 1 onion, chopped

 1.2 litres vegetable stock (ensure gluten free)

 3 celery sticks, diced

1 red pepper, de-seeded and diced

 1 yellow pepper, de-seeded and diced

2 teaspoons ground cumin

a pinch of dried chilli flakes

2 tablespoons tomato purée

400 g can chopped tomatoes

410 g can kidney beans in water, drained and rinsed

198 g can sweetcorn, drained

juice of ½ lime

3 tablespoons chopped fresh coriander

This hearty soup is packed with filling pulses and vegetables to keep you feeling satisfied.

Place the onion in a large lidded saucepan with 100 ml of the stock. Cover and cook for 3 minutes then add the celery and peppers. Cover again and cook for a further 5 minutes.

Add the cumin, chilli flakes and tomato purée and cook for 1 minute, stirring, to bring out the flavour, before adding the chopped tomatoes and the rest of the stock. Bring back to the boil and simmer for 10 minutes.

Add the kidney beans and sweetcorn to the soup and simmer for 5 minutes. Mix in the lime juice and serve the soup scattered with the coriander.

Cook's tips Cooking an onion in stock instead of oil at the beginning of a recipe means you can save *ProPoints* values but still end up with a sweet and softened onion flavour.

To cut down on preparation time, the next time you are chopping onions or peppers, chop a few extra and store each onion or pepper in an individual plastic food bag in the freezer, ready to use in future.

Thai VEGETABLE Broth

  ProPoints value per serving
ProPoints values per recipe 1

Serves 1
Takes 15 minutes

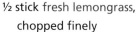

75 g mushrooms, sliced
½ red chilli, de-seeded and sliced
½ stick fresh lemongrass,
    chopped finely
1 cm fresh root ginger, peeled
    and cut into matchsticks
400 ml vegetable stock (ensure
    gluten free)
1 tablespoon soy sauce (ensure
    gluten free)
50 g baby corn, sliced
40 g mange tout, halved
juice of ½ lime
2 tablespoons chopped fresh
    coriander

With its colourful ingredients and blend of hot and sour flavours, this aromatic soup not only tastes amazing, it looks great too.

Place the mushrooms, chilli, lemongrass and ginger in a lidded saucepan with 2 tablespoons of the stock. Cover and cook for 4 minutes.

Add the rest of the stock, the soy sauce and baby corn, cover the pan again and cook for 3 minutes. Add the mange tout and cook for a final 2 minutes.

Stir the lime juice into the soup, ladle into a bowl and serve scattered with the coriander.

Variations

You can make the soup into a more substantial supper dish by adding 100 g cooked, peeled tiger prawns for 3 **ProPoints** values per serving, or 100 g cooked skinless chicken breast for 5 **ProPoints** values per serving.

> **Cook's tip** You're unlikely to use a whole packet of lemongrass in any recipe so chop the remaining lemongrass and store it in a plastic food bag in the freezer, ready to use another time.

Quorn TIKKA Salad

4 *ProPoints* values per serving
ProPoints values per recipe 8

Serves 2
Takes 20 minutes

5 tablespoons low fat natural
    yogurt
1 teaspoon tikka curry powder
140 g meat-free roast-style sliced
    fillets
a small handful of fresh mint or
    coriander leaves
75 g mixed salad leaves
8 radishes
1 small red onion
¼ cucumber
8 cherry tomatoes

This Indian-influenced salad is perfect to take to work.

Put 2 tablespoons of the yogurt into a shallow bowl and stir in the tikka powder. Add the meat-free roast-style sliced fillets and stir to coat thoroughly.

Put the remaining yogurt in a small bowl. Chop some of the mint or coriander finely and stir into the yogurt. Set aside.

Share the salad leaves between 2 serving plates. Thinly slice the radishes, red onion and cucumber and arrange an equal amount over each salad. Halve the cherry tomatoes and divide between the salads. Spoon the meat-free fillets on top of the salads and drizzle them with the yogurt dressing.

Cook's tip To save time, you could slice the radishes, red onion and cucumber in your food processor, fitted with the slicer attachment.

Bubble & SQUEAK with Poached Egg

A great way to use up leftover potatoes but also quick to make from scratch for a light supper.

 Serves 1
Takes 30 minutes

125 g potatoes, cut into large
    chunks
50 g Savoy cabbage, shredded
3 spring onions, sliced
½ teaspoon Dijon mustard (ensure
    gluten free)
calorie controlled cooking spray
a dash of white wine vinegar
1 very fresh egg
salt and freshly ground black
    pepper

Boil the potatoes until soft when pierced with a knife. At the same time, set a steamer above the pan and cook the cabbage for 4–5 minutes. Add the spring onions to the steamer for the last 2 minutes to soften. Drain and mash the potatoes, add the cabbage, spring onions and mustard, season and mix well. Shape into 2 patties.

Heat a non-stick frying pan and mist with the cooking spray. Cook the patties over a low heat for 6–8 minutes, turning once.

Meanwhile, bring a small saucepan of water up to a fast boil, add the vinegar and carefully crack the egg into the water. Simmer for 3–4 minutes until the egg is cooked to your liking. Serve immediately with the patties.

> *Cook's tip* The fresher the egg, the better it will keep its shape in the water.

TORTILLA
Española

4 *ProPoints* values per serving
ProPoints values per recipe 22

Serves 6
Takes 35–40 minutes

2 teaspoons olive oil
1 onion, sliced finely
500 g waxy potatoes, such as
    Charlotte
4 eggs
salt and freshly ground black
    pepper

Delicious served with a tomato and onion salad for no extra *ProPoints* values, and perfect for a packed lunch or picnic.

Heat the oil in an 18 cm non-stick frying pan and fry the onion on a medium heat for 15 minutes, or until soft and slightly coloured.

Meanwhile, peel the potatoes and cook in boiling water until nearly tender, about 15 minutes. Drain and cut into 5 mm slices. Add to the onions and mix together. Try not to break up the potatoes.

Preheat the grill to hot. Beat the eggs in a jug and season well. Pour over the potatoes and cook on a medium heat until the egg is nearly set and is coming away from the edges. Remove from the heat and place under the hot grill to finish cooking the tortilla. Once golden and cooked through, remove from the pan and leave to cool before cutting into 6 slices to serve.

> *Cook's tip* When placing the frying pan under the grill, be aware that the handle may get hot, so make sure you use an oven glove to remove the pan from the heat.

Roast Vegetable & GIANT Couscous Salad

 7 *ProPoints* values per serving
ProPoints values per recipe 15

 Serves 2
 Preparation time 10 minutes
 Cooking time 15–20 minutes

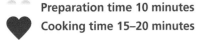

1 red onion, cut into quarters
1 yellow pepper, de-seeded and
   chopped roughly
1 courgette, chopped roughly
2 garlic cloves, crushed
1 tablespoon balsamic vinegar
2 teaspoons olive oil
2 fresh rosemary sprigs
125 g wholewheat giant couscous
2 teaspoons capers
juice of ½ lemon
salt and freshly ground black
   pepper
mixed salad leaves, to serve

This versatile salad goes really well with some crisp mixed salad leaves, for no extra *ProPoints* values – whether you're on the go or relaxing at home.

Preheat the oven to Gas Mark 5/190°C/fan oven 170°C. Place the prepared vegetables on a non-stick baking tray and drizzle over the vinegar and olive oil. Add the rosemary and some seasoning and roast for 15–20 minutes, or until the vegetables are soft and just starting to caramelise.

Meanwhile, place the couscous in a pan of boiling water and cook for 7–9 minutes, or until tender. Drain and tip into a serving bowl.

Stir the capers and lemon juice into the couscous together with some seasoning, add the roasted vegetables, then serve warm or cold with the salad leaves.

Pasta Salad with PEAS & Garlicky Tomatoes

6 *ProPoints* **values per serving**
ProPoints **values per recipe 11**

Serves 2
Takes 15 minutes

100 g wholewheat fusilli pasta
60 g frozen petits pois
1 teaspoon extra virgin olive oil
1 garlic clove, crushed
250 g cherry tomatoes, halved
a squeeze of lemon juice, plus
   lemon wedges to serve
a handful of fresh basil leaves
salt and freshly ground black
   pepper

A super-speedy pasta dish that you can have on the table in under 20 minutes. Alternatively, let it cool and take it to work in a lunchbox — job done!

Cook the pasta following the packet instructions. Add the peas for the final 2 minutes then drain and set aside in a colander.

Return the pan to the heat and add the oil, garlic and tomatoes. Toss together briefly to soften the tomatoes slightly, then return the pasta and peas to the pan and stir.

Add the lemon juice, season to taste, stir the basil through and serve with lemon wedges.

BEANIE Burgers
with *Salsa*

 ProPoints values per serving
ProPoints values per recipe 5

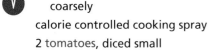 **Serves 2**
Takes 20 minutes

240 g flageolet or haricot beans,
   rinsed and drained

1 egg white

½ tablespoon medium curry powder
   (ensure gluten free)

4 spring onions, chopped

75 g carrot, peeled and grated
   coarsely

calorie controlled cooking spray

2 tomatoes, diced small

salt and freshly ground black
   pepper

These curried bean and vegetable burgers are so simple to make and much tastier than ready-made versions.

Tip the beans into a food processor with the egg white and curry powder. Season and pulse until mixed, but without processing to a smooth paste.

Stir in half the spring onions and the grated carrot and mix briefly.

Use damp hands to shape the sticky mixture into 4 burgers.

Spray a non-stick frying pan with the cooking spray and fry the burgers for 5 minutes each side over a medium heat.

Meanwhile, mix the tomatoes with the remaining spring onions and season. Serve the salsa spooned over the hot burgers.

Cook's tip The uncooked burger mixture can be frozen. Simply shape and wrap in cling film and freeze for up to 3 months. Defrost thoroughly in the fridge before cooking.

Potato, CUCUMBER & DILL Salad

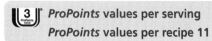

ProPoints values per serving
ProPoints values per recipe 11

Serves 4
Takes 25 minutes

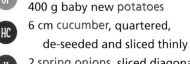
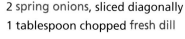

400 g baby new potatoes
6 cm cucumber, quartered,
    de-seeded and sliced thinly
2 spring onions, sliced diagonally
1 tablespoon chopped fresh dill

For the dressing
4 tablespoons fat-free fromage frais
1 teaspoon wholegrain mustard
    (ensure gluten free)
2 teaspoons lemon juice
salt and freshly ground black
    pepper

This crisp, summery salad goes really well with cooked meats, fish and barbecued food, and the dill brings a lovely fresh, and different, taste to the usual potato salad.

Bring a saucepan of water to the boil, add the potatoes and cook for 10 minutes or until tender then drain. Transfer to a serving bowl and leave to cool slightly. Add the cucumber and spring onions to the bowl.

To make the dressing, mix together the fromage frais, mustard and lemon juice. Season and spoon the dressing over the potato salad. Turn until coated. Serve sprinkled with dill.

TOASTY Porridge with *Spiced Apple* Compote

6 ProPoints values per serving
ProPoints values per recipe 11

♥ **Serves 2**
Takes 15 minutes

1 cooking apple, peeled and
    chopped
1 teaspoon lemon juice
1 clove
a pinch of ground cinnamon (or a
    small piece of cinnamon stick)
artificial sweetener, to taste
60 g porridge oats
400 ml skimmed milk

To serve
a splash of cold skimmed milk
    (optional)
2 heaped teaspoons 0% fat natural
    Greek yogurt
a pinch of ground mixed spice

Get your day off to the perfect start with this energy-boosting breakfast packed with oaty goodness.

Place the apple in a small lidded saucepan with the lemon juice, a teaspoon of water and the clove and cinnamon. Cover and cook gently for 5 minutes, or until the apple starts to break up (add another teaspoon of water if it looks dry), then stir in the sweetener to taste. Cover to keep warm.

Meanwhile, put the oats in a non-stick pan and toast them over a medium-high heat for a couple of minutes, or until fragrant. Add the milk, turn the heat down and slowly bring to the boil, stirring with a wooden spoon. Simmer on the lowest heat, stirring often, for 8–10 minutes, or until cooked and creamy. Spoon into 2 bowls and top each with half of the apple compote and a splash of cold milk, if desired. Serve each bowl with a spoonful of yogurt and a sprinkle of mixed spice.

> *Cook's tip* You can make the compote a day or two ahead. To speed up this recipe, omit the toasting stage and just microwave the oats and milk on high in a deep bowl for 2 minutes per portion. Stir well, then leave to cool a little before serving.

Raspberry JELLY *Creams*

Makes 4

Takes 10 minutes + 30 minutes infusing + setting

Approx. 200 g blueberries

Approx. 200 g raspberries

5 fruit tea bags, e.g. raspberry, blackberry and cranberry

1 sachet sugar free raspberry jelly powder (ensure gluten free)

For the cream

40 g raspberries, fresh or frozen

150 g quark

1–2 teaspoons artificial sweetener, to taste

1 teaspoon vanilla extract

Using infused tea bags as the base, these jelly creams are really lovely as a light dessert. Try serving them in different designed glasses like we have — they'll look great!

Put a handful of mixed berries in the bottom of 4 glasses or ramekins, reserving a few to decorate the tops.

In a saucepan, bring 300 ml water to the boil with the fruit tea bags, cover and leave to infuse for 30 minutes.

Empty the contents of the jelly sachet into a bowl and bring the tea-infused water back to the boil, removing the tea bags first. Add to the jelly and stir, then add 300 ml cold water. Once the jelly is fully dissolved, pour into the 4 glasses. Place in the fridge to set.

Once the jelly is set, make the cream. Place the raspberries in a sieve over a bowl and press through with a spoon to remove the seeds. Add the quark, sweetener and vanilla extract to the bowl, and mix gently until smooth. Divide over the jellies and top with the reserved berries.

Baked BANANA with *Passion Fruit*

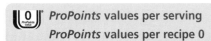

ProPoints values per serving
ProPoints values per recipe 0

Serves 1
Takes 10 minutes

1 orange, peeled and sliced
1 banana, peeled and sliced thickly
1 passion fruit
1 tablespoon fat-free natural yogurt

Passion fruit adds a wonderful, exotic fragrance to this easy fruit parcel.

Preheat the oven to Gas Mark 6/200°C/fan oven 180°C.

Place a large square of foil on a baking tray. Sit the orange slices in the centre, add the banana then scoop the seeds from the passion fruit and place on the banana.

Close the parcel tightly, crimping and sealing the foil so that the juices can't escape. Bake for 7 minutes, then open up carefully and serve topped with the yogurt.

Warm SUMMER BERRIES with *Raspberry* Sauce

 ProPoints values per serving
ProPoints values per recipe 0

This fabulous fruit combo is a zero-hero! Mixed berries make a stunning dessert — or try just as a snack on their own when you need a quick pick-me-up. You could also try serving with 150 g 0% fat natural Greek yogurt per person for 2 **ProPoints** values per serving.

 Serves 2
Takes 15 minutes

 200 g strawberries

 100 g mixed berries, such as raspberries, blackberries and blueberries

 100 g raspberries, to serve

Preheat the oven to Gas Mark 4/180°C/fan oven 160°C.

Hull and halve the strawberries and put them in a baking dish with the mixed berries. Bake for 6–8 minutes.

Meanwhile, purée the raspberries with 3 tablespoons of water with a hand-held blender or blender. Serve with the warm fruit.

INDEX